The Space Swap Shop

By Jenny Jinks

Illustrated by
Aditi Kakade
Beaufrand

Chapter 1

"What's that?!" cried Zork, as a piece of scrap metal whizzed straight towards his rocket. He swerved left and dodged it, but only just in time.

More space junk whizzed past him as he headed for home.

There was so much old rubbish floating around in space it was getting hard to go anywhere.

"That was a close one," Zork said as he finally landed safely back on Planet Pik. "Wow, space is a mess."

But the next time Zork went out, he wasn't so lucky.

He was happily zipping about when a huge piece of rubbish crashed right into the side of his old blue jet.

"Whoa!" Zork cried.

The jet went spinning out of control and then spluttered to a stop.

Zork tried the engine, but it wouldn't start. He was stuck. And his jet was in bits.

Chapter 2

Zork's jet was towed back to Planet Pik.

Zork took it to a mechanic. The mechanic took one look at Zork's jet and shook his head.

"It will cost a lot of money to fix that," he said. But Zork didn't have much money. It would take him forever to save up enough to get the jet fixed.

"What am I going to do?" said Zork.

"It's okay," the mechanic said. "Just get a new one. That one was old anyway."

But Zork didn't want a new jet. He liked his blue one. It might be a little old and rusty, but it was the first jet he had ever had.

He stared up at all the rubbish already swirling around up above him. If he scrapped his jet it would just end up out there, adding to the problem. He didn't want that. Besides, he couldn't bear to think of his jet floating around in space with all the other unwanted junk.

That's when Zork had a brilliant idea.

Space was full of old abandoned jets, just like his. What if all the parts he needed to fix his jet were just up there waiting for him?

He borrowed a spare rocket and zoomed off, looking for anything he thought he might need.

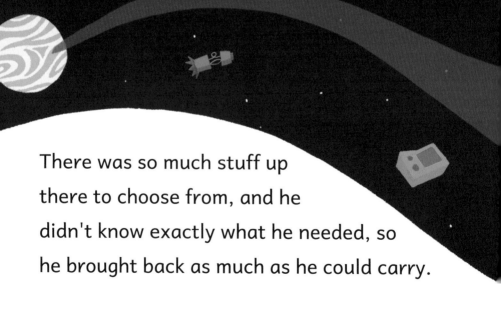

There was so much stuff up there to choose from, and he didn't know exactly what he needed, so he brought back as much as he could carry.

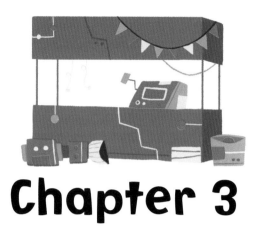

Chapter 3

Zork got straight to work on fixing his jet.

He sorted through the pile of junk. He had found some amazing things, and some of it even looked brand new. He couldn't understand why people had got rid of it.

He found buttons and mirrors, lights and switches. He even got a brand new shiny bell to put on the front. He had always wanted a bell!

But he still needed a few more bits to fix the jet. It was time to go out and collect some more space junk.

Zork collected even more than last time. It was a bit easier to find what he was looking for, now that there was less space junk floating around everywhere.

He hammered and he banged, he glued and
he welded. Before long, his jet was looking
just as good as before.

Actually, Zork thought it looked even better.
But when he pressed the button on his jet,
the engine still wouldn't start.

Chapter 4

Zork was making such a racket that his friend, Barg, came to see what he was doing.

"I'm trying to fix my jet," Zork sighed. "I've put lots of new parts in it, but it still won't start. Maybe it is just a load of junk."

"Can I have a look?" Barg asked. She inspected Zork's jet. "Ah, I know just the thing you need to make that start. I'll just go and get it."

Barg rushed home, then came back with a tiny metal part. She popped it into the engine. "Give that a try."

Zork pressed the button. Straight away the engine roared into life.

"Thanks!" said Zork. He was thrilled. "How much do you want for it?"

"Oh you can have it, I was only going to throw it away."

Zork couldn't believe his jet was finally fixed. And it hadn't cost him a thing!

Barg started looking around at all the rest of the stuff Zork had collected.

"You've got some really interesting stuff here," said Barg. She picked something up off the pile. "Hey, I've been looking for one of these for ages, they're really rare. Can I buy it off you?"

Zork looked at it and shrugged. He didn't even know what is was. It wasn't any use to him now he had his jet working again.

"You can have it if you want," Zork said. "Take anything you like. It's all just junk."

"One Pikling's junk is another Pikling's treasure!" Barg said, and she picked up several bits and went home very happy.

Chapter 5

Zork thought about what Barg had said: 'one Pikling's junk is another Pikling's treasure'.

Maybe Barg was right. All that junk was just floating around up in space. But what if someone could use it? He was sure lots of other Piklings would rather fix things than throw them away. They just needed to be able find the bits they needed.

That gave Zork a brilliant idea. He zoomed off in his jet to get everything ready. Zork put posters up all over Pik. They said:

SPACE SWAP SHOP

Got something to fix?
Got things you don't want?

Then come on down to Zork's
Super Space Swap Shop!

You can swap the things you don't want
for the things you need.

Chapter 6

Zork was nervous as he set everything up.

He waited. What if nobody came?

But soon Piklings started to arrive.

At first, there was only a few. They came because they were curious. They had never heard of a swap shop before. They didn't know what to expect.

"So I can just bring my unwanted things here instead of dumping them in space?" one Pikling asked.

"And I can just take whatever I want?" another said.

"That's right," said Zork.

Nobody could believe it.

It was so simple, why hadn't they thought of it before?

Soon, Zork's Swap Shop was the busiest place on Planet Pik.

Piklings didn't buy as many new things anymore. They knew they could find pretty much anything they needed at Zork's.
And if anyone had any rubbish, they didn't just dump it in space any more. They took it to Zork's Swap Shop so that someone else could use it.

Soon Zork had got rid of almost all of the rubbish from his home. So he went exploring to collect junk from further away.

Zork loved exploring space. And space had never looked so tidy.

The End

Book Bands for Guided Reading

The Institute of Education book banding system is a scale of colours that reflects the various levels of reading difficulty. The bands are assigned by taking into account the content, the language style, the layout and phonics. Word, phrase and sentence level work is also taken into consideration.

Maverick Early Readers are a bright, attractive range of books covering the pink to white bands. All of these books have been book banded for guided reading to the industry standard and edited by a leading educational consultant.

Pink
Red
Yellow
Blue
Green
Orange
Turquoise
Purple
Gold
White

To view the whole Maverick Readers scheme, visit our website at

www.maverickearlyreaders.com

Or scan the QR code above to view our scheme instantly!